Dumplings Mean Family

By Jennifer Shaw

Illustrated by Rinnah Shaw

To Noah Bǎolóng, Ethan Lóngníng, and Anna Rúxuān -
our family wouldn't be complete without you!

ISBN: 978-0-9839591-3-7 (hardcover)
    978-0-9839591-2-0 (paperback)
Library of Congress Control Number: 2021931554

Illustrated by Rinnah Shaw
Printed in the U.S.A.

Dumplings Mean Family

By Jennifer Shaw

Illustrated by Rinnah Shaw

Hi, my name is Ethan.
I have a big family.

你好!
Nǐ hǎo!

Some of us were born in China, and some of us were born in the United States.

When my brother and sister and I were little, we lived in China. We lived in different cities and had different caregivers. We didn't have parents of our own. We ate many common Chinese foods like dumplings and whole steamed fish and noodles.

China

When we got older, our new parents came to China and adopted us into their family!

It was very scary to leave China, but I was also happy to have a family of my own.

When we got to the United States, so many things were different! The language, the schools, the houses, the holidays - even the people looked different.

But one thing that was SO different was the food!

When we first got to our new home, we were worried we would never have yummy food again! Our parents could cook, but they only knew how to make American food.

We wondered why American food came in such big pieces, and why it was all so dry without sauce. And why did Americans separate their food into piles and eat with forks? It was too different for us. We missed Chinese food.

My brother asked my mom to make dumplings. Everyone in China eats dumplings. But our new mom said she didn't know how!

We were shocked! We thought every parent would know how to make dumplings!
We thought we would never eat dumplings again.

My mom said she would buy some at the grocery store.

They were okay, but they weren't the same. They were bland and mushy from the freezer, and they didn't taste right. My mom saw how sad we were. Not having the dumplings we remembered was making us homesick for China.

My mom said, "Let's learn to make dumplings!"
She asked us about our favorite kinds, and looked up different recipes.
Then she called her friends for help.
We went to Mr. and Mrs. Cheung's house to practice.

They showed us how to make fresh filling from scratch, and taught us different ways to fold them.
When the dumplings were done, they were so delicious!
Just like we remembered!

My mom thought we were ready to try it on our own.

Napa Cabbage
白菜
Báicài

Dumpling Wrappers
饺子皮
Jiǎozi Pí

She made the filling first. Next, she set out stacks of dumpling wrappers for everyone, and little bowls of water to seal them. Then we had a dumpling party!

All the kids folded and pinched the wrappers around the filling while my parents cooked the dumplings. We ate them while we worked! We tried them boiled and pan fried and steamed. We ate them with vinegar and soy sauce and chili oil.

They were so yummy and our family laughed so much together as we folded and ate dumplings.

Now my family loves to cook so many Chinese foods.
We learned to make them all together!
We prepare dumplings for my brother and whole
steamed fish for me and noodles for my little sister.
We have also found American foods we like.
It's good to like different things!

My parents say our family is American and our family is Chinese. We are proud to be both.

We may be different in some ways, but we are one family.

The Shaw Family

This book was made possible in part by the generosity of Madison Adoption Associates, the adoption agency that helped the Shaw family to bring Ethan and his sister, Anna, home. For this, the Shaws are eternally grateful.

If your family is considering adoption, please contact Madison Adoption Associates, one of the most highly rated adoption agencies in the world. Their mission is to bring hope, love, and connection by serving children, individuals, and families in the areas of adoption, foster care, and support services.

Madison Adoption Associates
Society Office Complex
1102 Society Drive
Claymont, DE 19703
Phone: 1 (302) 475-8977
contact@madisonadoption.org
madisonadoption.org

Vocabulary

Hello	你好 (Nǐ hǎo)
China	中国 (Zhōngguó)
United States	美国 (Měiguó)
Dad	爸爸 (Bàba)
Mom	妈妈 (Māmā)
Big Brother	哥哥 (Gēgē)
Little Brother	弟弟 (Dìdì)
Big Sister	姐姐 (Jiějiě)
Little Sister	妹妹 (Mèimei)
Dumplings	饺子 (Jiǎozi)
Fish	鱼 (Yú)
Noodles	面条 (Miàntiáo)
Let's eat!	我们吃饭吧 (Wǒmen chīfàn ba)
Yummy!	好吃 (Hào chī)

Shaw Family Pork Dumpling Recipe*

Ingredients

1 small napa cabbage
Salt
1½ tsp. fresh ginger, minced
¼ cup sliced green onions
¼ tsp. ground white
     pepper powder
3 tbsp. soy sauce
1 tbsp. rice vinegar
2 tbsp. rice wine
2 tsp. sesame oil
1 lb. ground pork
1 package round dumpling
     wrappers, northern or
     "Shanghai" style.

*Recipe adapted from multiple northern Chinese recipes. Pork and cabbage is a very traditional dumpling filling and the Shaw kids' favorite, but there are many kinds. Visit *dumplingsmeanfamily.com* for step-by-step video instructions to make these dumplings at home!

Finely chop the cabbage or pulse in a food processor. Remove the cabbage and put it in a bowl. Sprinkle liberally with salt. Mix, then let it sit for at least 10 minutes.

Combine the ginger, green onions, white pepper powder, soy sauce, rice vinegar, rice wine, and sesame oil in a food processor and pulse one or two times. Add the pork to the food processor and pulse just until combined. If you don't have a food processor, you can do this by hand and the filling will just be a little chunkier.

The cabbage should now have released a lot of water. Squeeze as much water out of the cabbage as possible with your hands (or even better, through a cheese cloth) and then combine with the pork mixture to complete your dumpling filling.

To make your dumplings, add about two teaspoons of filling to the center of a dumpling wrapper. Trace a line of water with your finger around the entire edge of the dumpling wrapper and then fold it in half, pinching and sealing the edges together to make a half circle around the filling. If this is difficult with your wrappers, you can add a little cornstarch to the water to help them stick. The dumplings can be boiled or steamed just like this. To pan fry them, you will need to make a few folds in the round edge to pull up the corners and help them "stand up."

These dumplings can be boiled (8-10 minutes), steamed (10-15 minutes), or pan fried. To pan fry, heat oil in a pan and fry the dumplings until the wrapper is golden brown on the bottom. Immediately add enough water to cover the bottom of the pan and put the lid on. Steam them, adding water as needed for an additional 8 minutes. Take the lid off and cook until the water is gone and the bottoms crisp up again. Enjoy!

Dumplings are always served with sauce. An easy one is equal parts soy sauce and rice vinegar, but there are many variations. This recipe makes 40-50 dumplings. The Shaw family often triples this recipe and freezes some for later.

Visit dumplingsmeanfamily.com for more amazing resources including:

- Ways your family can **help a child in need** right now -

- A step-by-step video to **make your own dumplings** at home -

- A behind-the-scenes look at **how this book was created** -

- Printable **coloring pages** from the book -

- Information about having **Jennifer Shaw visit your school** or group -

...and much more!

About the Author:

Jennifer Shaw is an award-winning author, speaker, singer, songwriter and five-time Top 40 Billboard artist. Her work has been featured by Focus on the Family, Insight for Living, Family Life Today, Compassion International, Autism Speaks, and many more. Her book, "Life Not Typical: How Special Needs Parenting Changed My Faith and My Song," has brought national attention to the issue of Sensory Processing Disorder. She lives in Columbus, Ohio with her husband, six busy kids, and two crazy dogs. Visit her on the web at jennifershaw.com.

About the Illustrator:

Rinnah Shaw is an up-and-coming illustrator and writer who was named "Illustrator of the Year" by Taylor University. Her art has been featured at the Metcalf Open, the McConnell Arts Center, Spring Arbor University Invitational, and the Garrett Museum of Art among others. She loves her large, busy family in Columbus, Ohio. Find more of her work on Instagram (@rinnah_draws) or on her website, rinnahshaw.com.